Back to Basics

MATHS

for 7–8 year olds

BOOK TWO

George Rodda

Number names

We are ten sheep

We are nine sheep

There are **nineteen** sheep altogether.

Write the answers in figures and words.

1 The number of black sheep is ☐ ☐ .

2 The number of white sheep is ☐ ☐ .

3 17 – 2 = ☐ ☐

Write these words in figures.

1 twenty-nine ☐   **2** sixty-six ☐   **3** forty-one ☐

4 one hundred and eleven ☐

5 two hundred ☐

Write these numbers in words.

1 28 ☐   **2** 18 ☐

3 49 ☐   **4** 94 ☐

5 55 ☐   **6** 700 ☐

Which number is the greater?

1 thirty or 41 ☐

2 3 tens or 2 hundreds ☐

3 twenty or fourteen ☐

4 9 tens and 4 or 8 tens and 9 ☐

2

Adding on

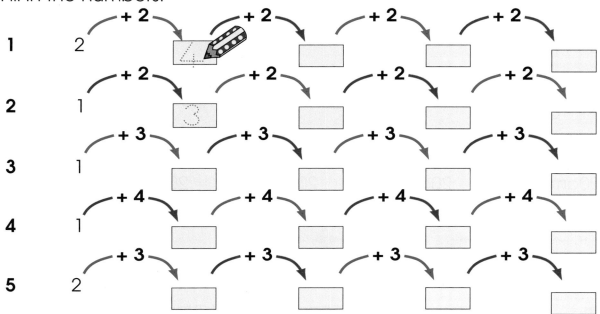

3   add 3   **+ 3** plus 3   6   add 3   **+ 3** plus 3   9   add 3   **+ 3** plus 3   12

Fill in the numbers.

1   2   +2 → 4   +2 → ☐   +2 → ☐   +2 → ☐

2   1   +2 → 3   +2 → ☐   +2 → ☐   +2 → ☐

3   1   +3 → ☐   +3 → ☐   +3 → ☐   +3 → ☐

4   1   +4 → ☐   +4 → ☐   +4 → ☐   +4 → ☐

5   2   +3 → ☐   +3 → ☐   +3 → ☐   +3 → ☐

Fill in these addition tables.

6

+	1	3	5	7
1		4		
3				
5	6			12

7

+	2	4	6	8
2				
4				
6				

8

+	2	3	4	5	6
7					
8					
9					
10					
11					

9

+	1	2	3	4	5
10					
12					
14					
16					
18					

Centimetres (cm)

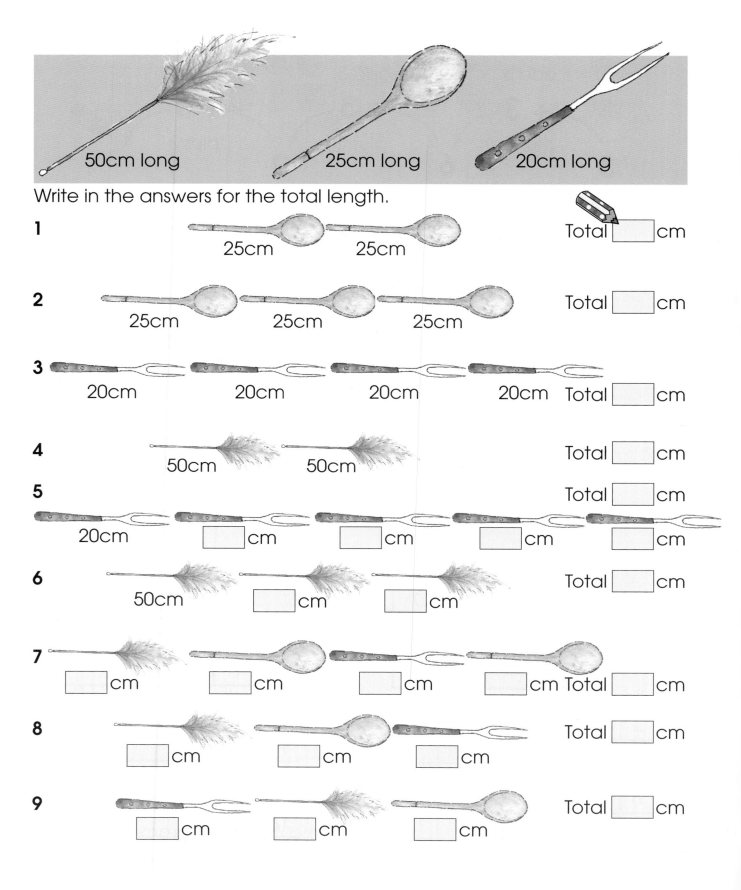

50cm long   25cm long   20cm long

Write in the answers for the total length.

1   25cm   25cm   Total ☐ cm

2   25cm   25cm   25cm   Total ☐ cm

3   20cm   20cm   20cm   20cm   Total ☐ cm

4   50cm   50cm   Total ☐ cm

5   20cm   ☐ cm   ☐ cm   ☐ cm   ☐ cm   Total ☐ cm

6   50cm   ☐ cm   ☐ cm   Total ☐ cm

7   ☐ cm   ☐ cm   ☐ cm   ☐ cm   Total ☐ cm

8   ☐ cm   ☐ cm   ☐ cm   Total ☐ cm

9   ☐ cm   ☐ cm   ☐ cm   Total ☐ cm

Plane shapes

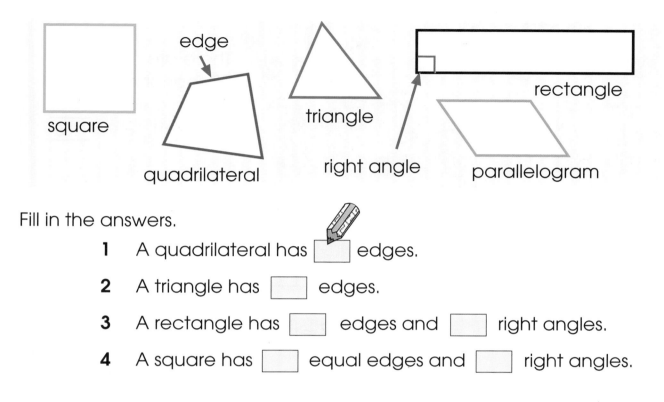

square

edge

quadrilateral

triangle

right angle

rectangle

parallelogram

Fill in the answers.

1 A quadrilateral has ☐ edges.

2 A triangle has ☐ edges.

3 A rectangle has ☐ edges and ☐ right angles.

4 A square has ☐ equal edges and ☐ right angles.

Use a ruler. Fill in the missing lengths and names.

5

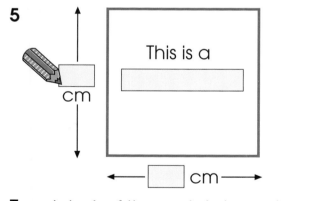

This is a

☐ cm

cm

6

☐ cm

This is a

☐ cm

7 Join 6 of these dots to make a rectangle.

. . . .

. . . .

. . . .

Find 4 rectangles.

8 Join 4 of these dots to make a parallelogram.

. . . . .

. . . . .

. . . . .

Find 4 parallelograms.

Take away

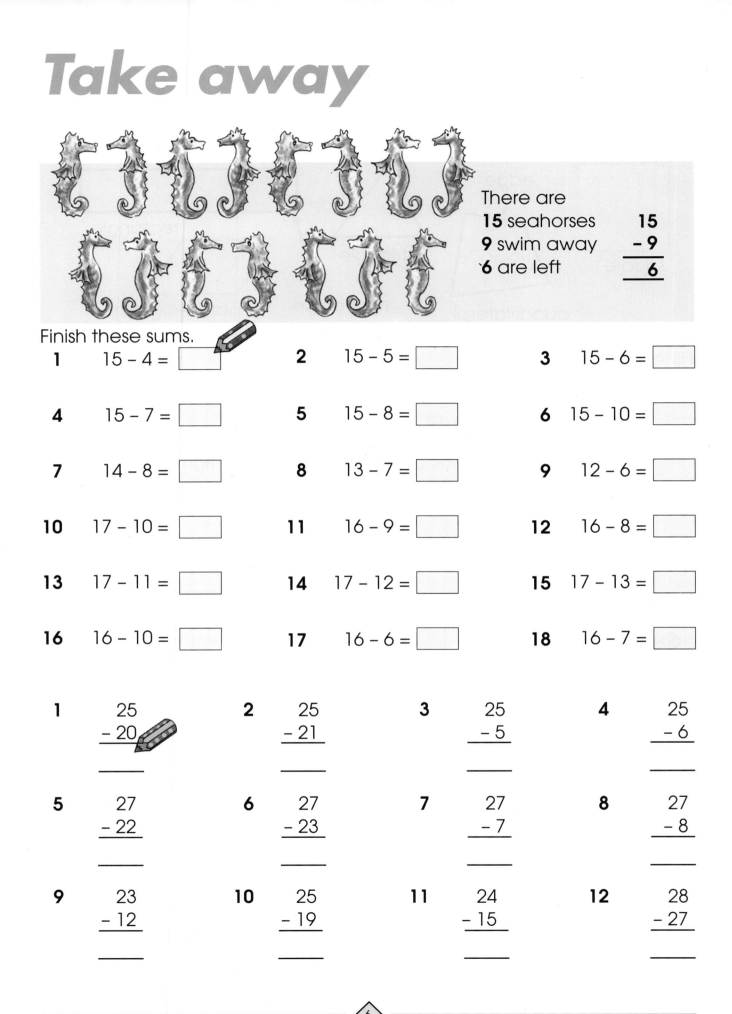

There are
15 seahorses   **15**
9 swim away   **− 9**
6 are left   **6**

Finish these sums.

1   15 − 4 = ☐   **2**   15 − 5 = ☐   **3**   15 − 6 = ☐

4   15 − 7 = ☐   **5**   15 − 8 = ☐   **6**   15 − 10 = ☐

7   14 − 8 = ☐   **8**   13 − 7 = ☐   **9**   12 − 6 = ☐

10   17 − 10 = ☐   **11**   16 − 9 = ☐   **12**   16 − 8 = ☐

13   17 − 11 = ☐   **14**   17 − 12 = ☐   **15**   17 − 13 = ☐

16   16 − 10 = ☐   **17**   16 − 6 = ☐   **18**   16 − 7 = ☐

1   25
    − 20

2   25
    − 21

3   25
    − 5

4   25
    − 6

5   27
    − 22

6   27
    − 23

7   27
    − 7

8   27
    − 8

9   23
    − 12

10   25
    − 19

11   24
    − 15

12   28
    − 27

Totals

12 eggs   11 eggs

$$\begin{array}{r} 12 \\ + 11 \\ \hline 23 \end{array}$$

12 + 11 = 23

12 add 11 = 23

12 plus 11 = 23

Work out these totals.

1
$$\begin{array}{r} 31 \\ + 9 \\ \hline \end{array}$$

2
$$\begin{array}{r} 13 \\ + 9 \\ \hline \end{array}$$

3
$$\begin{array}{r} 90 \\ + 13 \\ \hline \end{array}$$

4
$$\begin{array}{r} 90 \\ + 31 \\ \hline \end{array}$$

5
$$\begin{array}{r} 31 \\ + 19 \\ \hline \end{array}$$

6
$$\begin{array}{r} 31 \\ + 91 \\ \hline \end{array}$$

7
$$\begin{array}{r} 131 \\ + 19 \\ \hline \end{array}$$

8
$$\begin{array}{r} 131 \\ + 91 \\ \hline \end{array}$$

Write in the total for the 3 egg numbers.

1   5   10   6
Total

2   20   10   30
Total

3   31   21   11
Total

4   9   8   7
Total

5   12   7   9
Total

6   15   5   20
Total

Fill in the answers.

1   27 plus 13 =

2   13 add 27 =

3   81 add 9 =

4   81 plus 19 =

Fair exchange

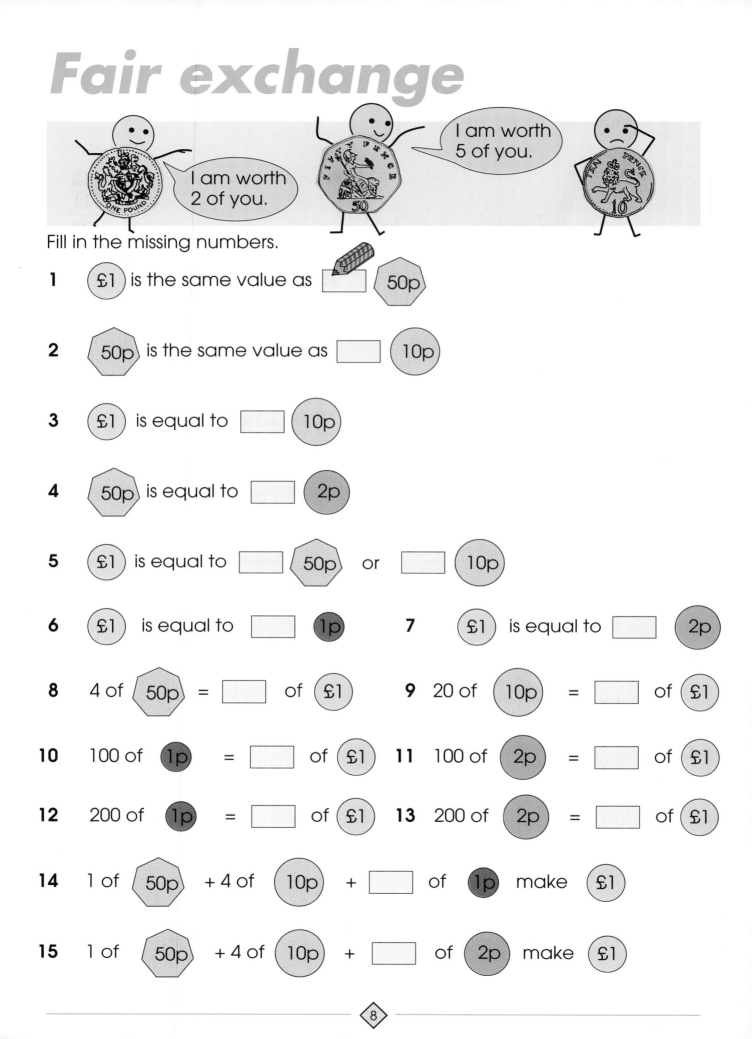

I am worth 2 of you.

I am worth 5 of you.

Fill in the missing numbers.

1 £1 is the same value as ☐ 50p

2 50p is the same value as ☐ 10p

3 £1 is equal to ☐ 10p

4 50p is equal to ☐ 2p

5 £1 is equal to ☐ 50p   or   ☐ 10p

6 £1 is equal to ☐ 1p   **7** £1 is equal to ☐ 2p

8 4 of 50p = ☐ of £1   **9** 20 of 10p = ☐ of £1

10 100 of 1p = ☐ of £1   **11** 100 of 2p = ☐ of £1

12 200 of 1p = ☐ of £1   **13** 200 of 2p = ☐ of £1

14 1 of 50p + 4 of 10p + ☐ of 1p make £1

15 1 of 50p + 4 of 10p + ☐ of 2p make £1

Substraction

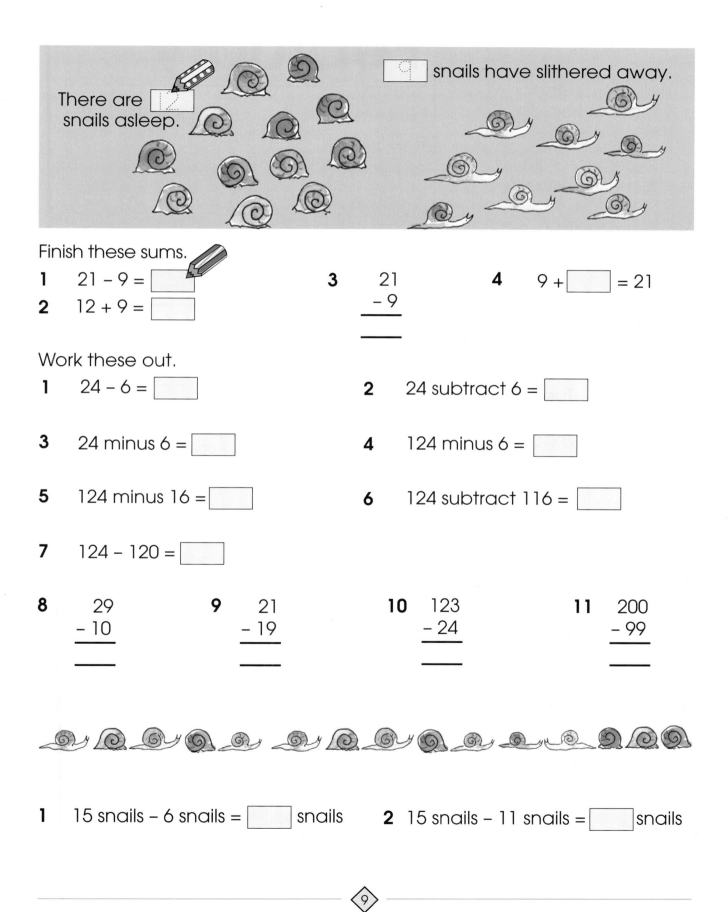

There are ☐ snails asleep. ☐ snails have slithered away.

Finish these sums.

1 21 – 9 = ☐

2 12 + 9 = ☐

3 21
     – 9
     ——

4 9 + ☐ = 21

Work these out.

1 24 – 6 = ☐

2 24 subtract 6 = ☐

3 24 minus 6 = ☐

4 124 minus 6 = ☐

5 124 minus 16 = ☐

6 124 subtract 116 = ☐

7 124 – 120 = ☐

8 29
     – 10
     ——

9 21
     – 19
     ——

10 123
     – 24
     ——

11 200
     – 99
     ——

1 15 snails – 6 snails = ☐ snails

2 15 snails – 11 snails = ☐ snails

Calendar months

This is a calendar page for February.

St Valentine's day is the 14th February.

In a leap year February has 29 days.

February					
Monday		5	12	19	26
Tuesday		6	13	20	27
Wednesday		7	14	21	28
Thursday	1	8	15	22	29
Friday	2	9	16	23	
Saturday	3	10	17	24	
Sunday	4	11	18	25	

Fill in the numbers.

1 In the calendar page there are ☐ Mondays.

2 ☐ Tuesdays **3** ☐ Wednesdays **4** ☐ Thursdays

5 ☐ Fridays **6** ☐ Saturdays **7** ☐ Sundays

8 This month has ☐ weeks ☐ days.

9 It has ☐ days because it is a leap year.

10 What day of the week is Valentine's day? ☐

11 Count on in twos and mark with a ✗ . 2, 4...

December					
Monday		9	16	23	30
Tuesday	3	10	17	24	31
Wednesday	4	11	18	25	
Thursday	5	12	19	26	
Friday	6	13	20	27	
Saturday	7	14	21	28	
Sunday	1	8	15	22	29

12 Count on in threes and mark with a ✗ . 3, 6...

March					
Monday		6	13	20	27
Tuesday		7	14	21	28
Wednesday	1	8	15	22	29
Thursday	2	9	16	23	30
Friday	3	10	17	24	31
Saturday	4	11	18	25	
Sunday	5	12	19	26	

+ or –

4 ◯+ 3 = 7   4 + 3   19 – 4   19 – ▢ = 15

0 1 2 3 4 5 6 7 8 9 **10** 11 12 13 14 15 16 17 18 19 **20**

These sums have either a number or a + or – missing.
Use the number line to help you finish them.

1   10 + 2 = ▢

2   10 – 2 = ▢

3   8 ◯ 2 = 10

4   12 ◯ 2 = 10

5   15 + 4 = ▢

6   15 ◯ 4 = 11

7   14 ◯ 7 = 7

8   14 + 7 = ▢

9   8 – 8 = ▢

10   8 ◯ 8 = 16

11   11 ◯ 9 = 20

12   9 – 8 = ▢

13   12 – 3 ◯ 3 = 6

14   12 – 3 ◯ 3 = 12

15   4 + 7 ◯ 7 = 4

16   14 ◯ 7 + 7 = 14

17
$$\begin{array}{r} 19 \\ -\ 12 \\ \hline \end{array}$$

18
$$\begin{array}{r} 19 \\ -\ \boxed{} \\ \hline 12 \end{array}$$

19
$$\begin{array}{r} 12 \\ +\ \boxed{} \\ \hline 19 \end{array}$$

20
$$\begin{array}{r} 12 \\ -\ \boxed{} \\ \hline 5 \end{array}$$

Fill in the missing signs.

1   2 ◯ 2 ◯ 2 ◯ 2 = 8

2   4 ◯ 4 ◯ 4 ◯ 4 = 8

3   5 ◯ 6 ◯ 4 ◯ 1 = 8

4   6 ◯ 5 ◯ 10 ◯ 1 = 10

Multiplication tables

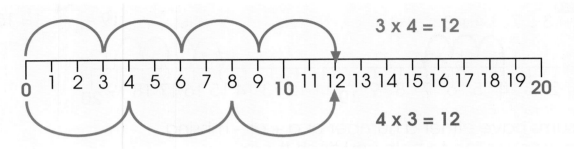

3 x 4 = 12

4 x 3 = 12

Fill in these tables.

1

x	1	2	3	4	5	6	7	8	9	10
3	3			12					27	

2

x	1	2	3	4	5	6	7	8	9	10
4										

3

x	1	2	3	4	5	6	7	8	9	10
5										

4

x	2	4	6	8
1				
3		12		
5			30	

5

x	0	1	3	5
1				
3				
5				

6

x	2	4	6
2			
4			
6			

7

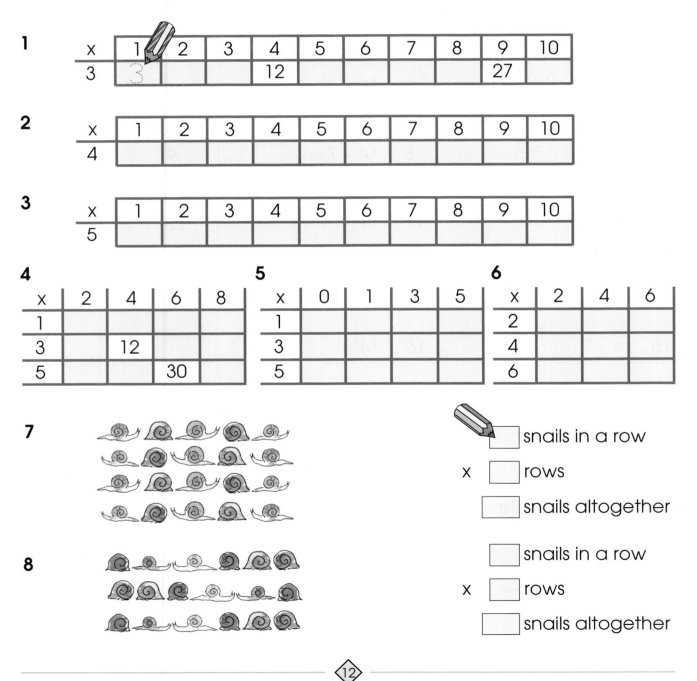

☐ snails in a row

x ☐ rows

☐ snails altogether

8

☐ snails in a row

x ☐ rows

☐ snails altogether

Fractions

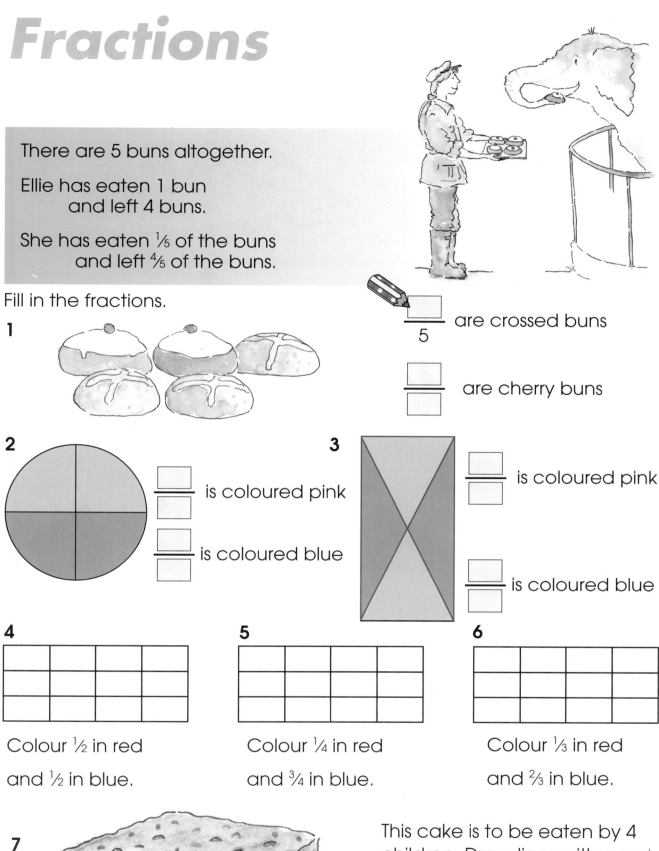

There are 5 buns altogether.

Ellie has eaten 1 bun
and left 4 buns.

She has eaten ⅕ of the buns
and left ⅘ of the buns.

Fill in the fractions.

1

$\dfrac{}{5}$ are crossed buns

$\dfrac{}{}$ are cherry buns

2

$\dfrac{}{}$ is coloured pink

$\dfrac{}{}$ is coloured blue

3

$\dfrac{}{}$ is coloured pink

$\dfrac{}{}$ is coloured blue

4

Colour ½ in red
and ½ in blue.

5

Colour ¼ in red
and ¾ in blue.

6

Colour ⅓ in red
and ⅔ in blue.

7

This cake is to be eaten by 4
children. Draw lines with a red
pencil to share the cake. Use a
green pencil to cut it in a
different way.

Doubles and trebles

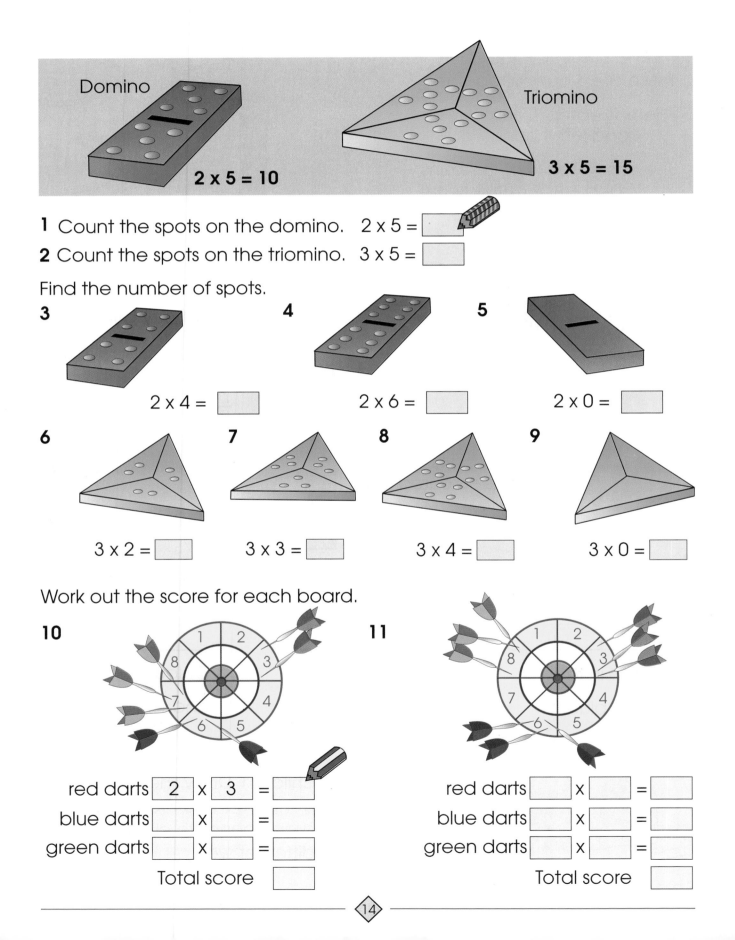

Domino

Triomino

2 x 5 = 10

3 x 5 = 15

1 Count the spots on the domino.   2 x 5 = ☐

2 Count the spots on the triomino.   3 x 5 = ☐

Find the number of spots.

3

2 x 4 = ☐

4

2 x 6 = ☐

5

2 x 0 = ☐

6

3 x 2 = ☐

7

3 x 3 = ☐

8

3 x 4 = ☐

9

3 x 0 = ☐

Work out the score for each board.

10

red darts   2 x 3 = ☐
blue darts ☐ x ☐ = ☐
green darts ☐ x ☐ = ☐
                Total score ☐

11

red darts   ☐ x ☐ = ☐
blue darts ☐ x ☐ = ☐
green darts ☐ x ☐ = ☐
                Total score ☐

Box of twelve

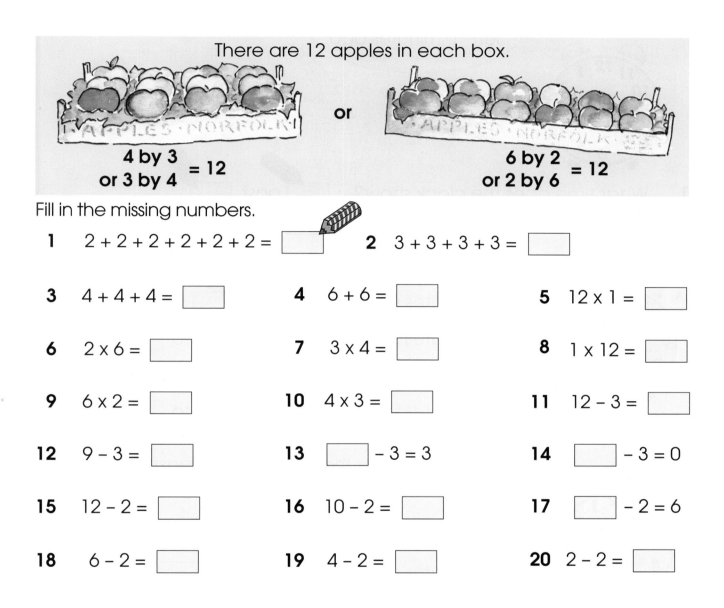

There are 12 apples in each box.

4 by 3
or 3 by 4 = 12

or

6 by 2
or 2 by 6 = 12

Fill in the missing numbers.

1 $2 + 2 + 2 + 2 + 2 + 2 =$ ☐   **2** $3 + 3 + 3 + 3 =$ ☐

3 $4 + 4 + 4 =$ ☐   **4** $6 + 6 =$ ☐   **5** $12 \times 1 =$ ☐

6 $2 \times 6 =$ ☐   **7** $3 \times 4 =$ ☐   **8** $1 \times 12 =$ ☐

9 $6 \times 2 =$ ☐   **10** $4 \times 3 =$ ☐   **11** $12 - 3 =$ ☐

12 $9 - 3 =$ ☐   **13** ☐ $- 3 = 3$ **14** ☐ $- 3 = 0$

15 $12 - 2 =$ ☐   **16** $10 - 2 =$ ☐   **17** ☐ $- 2 = 6$

18 $6 - 2 =$ ☐   **19** $4 - 2 =$ ☐   **20** $2 - 2 =$ ☐

Use a ruler to help you colour:

21 4cm red   4cm blue   4cm green

22 3cm red   3cm blue   3cm green   3cm yellow

Fast and slow

The 9 o'clock train left 10 minutes ago.

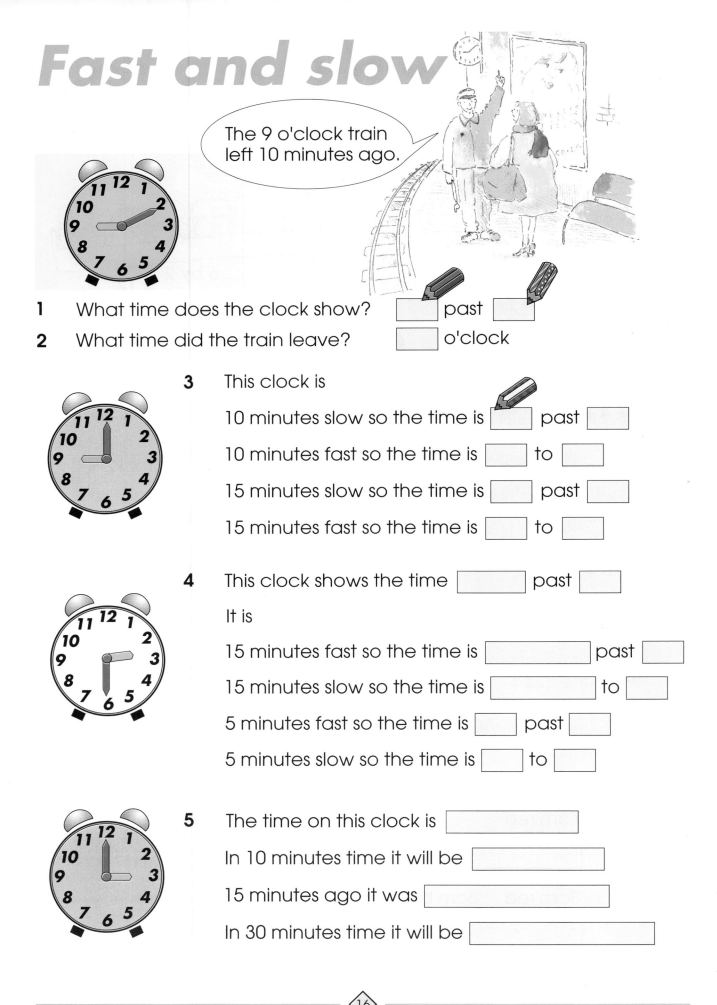

1   What time does the clock show? ☐ past ☐

2   What time did the train leave? ☐ o'clock

3   This clock is

10 minutes slow so the time is ☐ past ☐

10 minutes fast so the time is ☐ to ☐

15 minutes slow so the time is ☐ past ☐

15 minutes fast so the time is ☐ to ☐

4   This clock shows the time ☐ past ☐

It is

15 minutes fast so the time is ☐ past ☐

15 minutes slow so the time is ☐ to ☐

5 minutes fast so the time is ☐ past ☐

5 minutes slow so the time is ☐ to ☐

5   The time on this clock is ☐

In 10 minutes time it will be ☐

15 minutes ago it was ☐

In 30 minutes time it will be ☐

Multiplication

How many sweets would you like?

2 x 4 or **4 x 2**

or **4 times 2** or **2 times 4**

or **2 multiplied by 4** or **4 multiplied by 2**

FRUIT ROCKS

Fill in the missing numbers.

1   4 times 2 = 2 + 2 + 2 + 2 = 4 x 2 = ☐

4 multiplied by 2 = 4 x 2 = ☐

2 multiplied by 4 = 2 x 4 = ☐

Work out these sums by filling in the numbers.

2   3 x 2 = ☐ + ☐ + ☐

= ☐

3   2 x 3 = ☐ + ☐

= ☐

4   4 x 3 = ☐

5   3 x 4 = ☐

4p

5p

6   4 apples cost 4 x 5p = ☐ p

7   5 sweets cost 5 x 4p = ☐ p

Fill in these tables.

8

	1	2	3	4	5	6	7	8	9	10	sweets
cost	4p	p	p	16p	p	p	p	p	p	p	

9

	1	2	3	4	5	6	7	8	9	10	apples
cost	5p	p	p	p	p	p	p	p	p	p	

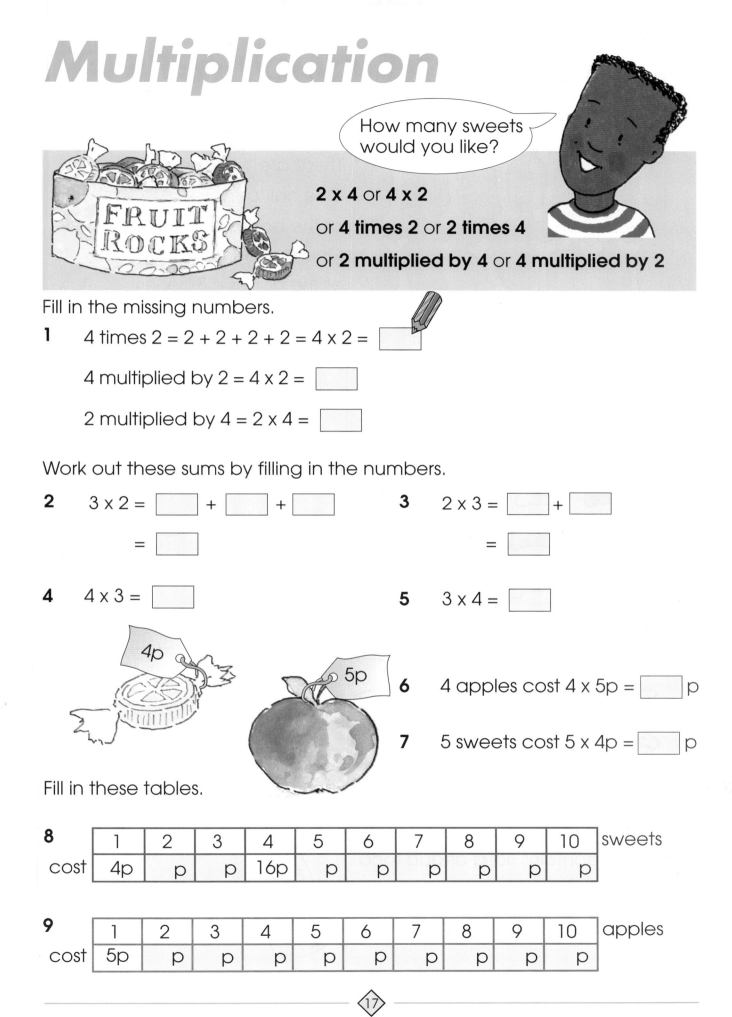

Halves and quarters

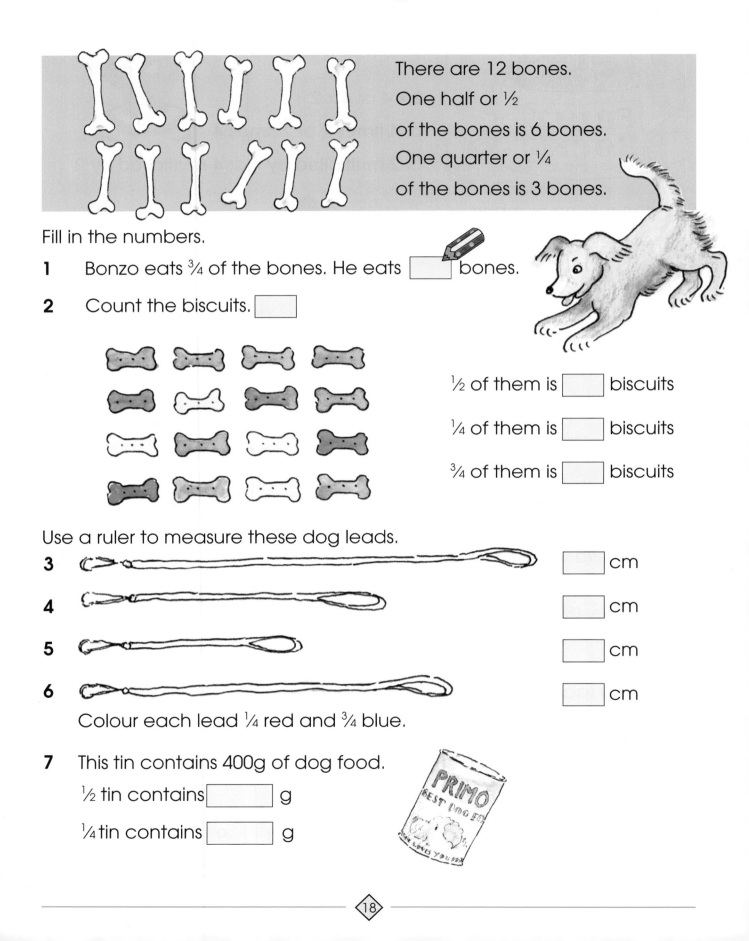

There are 12 bones.
One half or ½
of the bones is 6 bones.
One quarter or ¼
of the bones is 3 bones.

Fill in the numbers.

1   Bonzo eats ¾ of the bones. He eats [   ] bones.

2   Count the biscuits. [   ]

½ of them is [   ] biscuits

¼ of them is [   ] biscuits

¾ of them is [   ] biscuits

Use a ruler to measure these dog leads.

3   [   ] cm

4   [   ] cm

5   [   ] cm

6   [   ] cm

Colour each lead ¼ red and ¾ blue.

7   This tin contains 400g of dog food.

½ tin contains [   ] g

¼ tin contains [   ] g

More or less

50p is **more than** 20p

20p is **less than** 50p

The **difference** is 30p.

50p – 20p = 30p

Write in the correct words from:

more than   less than   equal to

1   40p [is _____] 50p   **2**   60p [is _____] 50p
The difference is [____] p   The difference is [____] p

3   30p [is _____] 50p   **4**   70p [is _____] 50p
The difference is [____] p   The difference is [____] p

5   10p [is _____] 50p   **6**   80p [is _____] 50p
The difference is [____] p   The difference is [____] p

7   50p [is _____] £1   **8**   £1 [is _____] 50p
The difference is [____] p   The difference is [____] p

9 100p [is _____] £1   **10** 100p [is _____] 99p
The difference is [____] p   The difference is [____] p

11

[is _____]

The difference is [____] p

Centimetres (cm) and millimetres (mm)

Measure and check the length of each tail.

1 White mouse ☐ cm
or ☐ mm

2 Yellow mouse ☐ cm
or ☐ mm

3 Pink mouse ☐ cm
or ☐ mm

4 Grey mouse ☐ cm
or ☐ mm

5 Which mouse has the longest tail? ☐

6 Which mouse has the shortest tail? ☐

Measure from mouse to mouse.

7 The two tails measure ☐ cm or ☐ mm.

8 The two tails measure ☐ cm or ☐ mm.

9 The two tails measure ☐ cm or ☐ mm.

10 The two tails measure ☐ cm or ☐ mm.

11 The white, pink, yellow and grey tails total ☐ cm.

Days and weeks

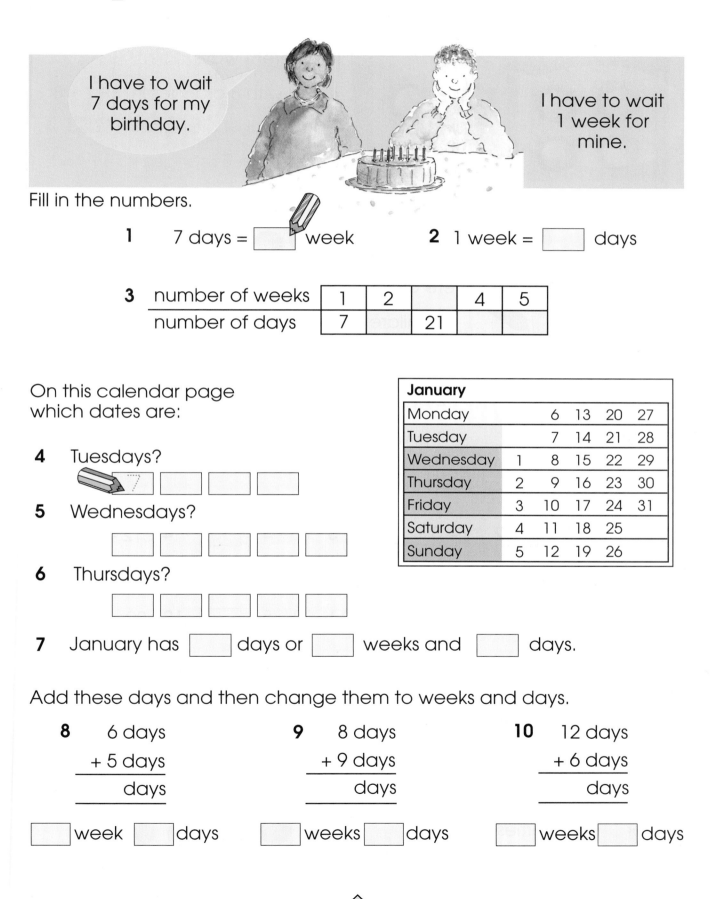

I have to wait 7 days for my birthday.

I have to wait 1 week for mine.

Fill in the numbers.

1　7 days = ☐ week　　**2**　1 week = ☐ days

3

number of weeks	1	2		4	5
number of days	7		21		

On this calendar page which dates are:

January					
Monday		6	13	20	27
Tuesday		7	14	21	28
Wednesday	1	8	15	22	29
Thursday	2	9	16	23	30
Friday	3	10	17	24	31
Saturday	4	11	18	25	
Sunday	5	12	19	26	

4　Tuesdays?

　　　☐7☐ ☐ ☐ ☐

5　Wednesdays?

　　　☐ ☐ ☐ ☐ ☐

6　Thursdays?

　　　☐ ☐ ☐ ☐ ☐

7　January has ☐ days or ☐ weeks and ☐ days.

Add these days and then change them to weeks and days.

8　　6 days
　　+ 5 days
　　———
　　　days

☐ week ☐ days

9　　8 days
　　+ 9 days
　　———
　　　days

☐ weeks ☐ days

10　12 days
　　+ 6 days
　　———
　　　days

☐ weeks ☐ days

21

Equal shares

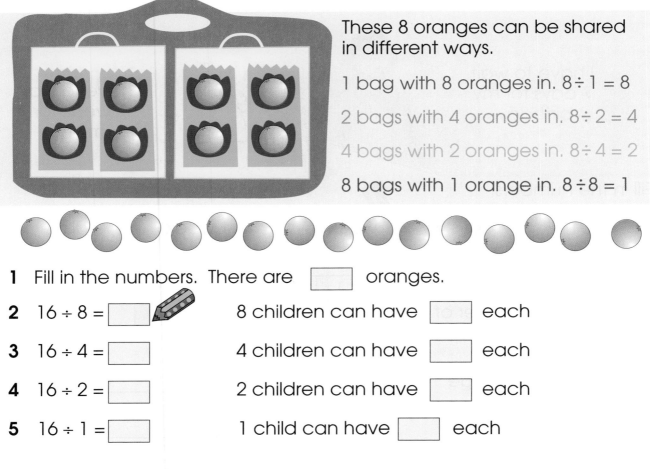

These 8 oranges can be shared in different ways.

1 bag with 8 oranges in. $8 \div 1 = 8$

2 bags with 4 oranges in. $8 \div 2 = 4$

4 bags with 2 oranges in. $8 \div 4 = 2$

8 bags with 1 orange in. $8 \div 8 = 1$

1 Fill in the numbers. There are ☐ oranges.

2 $16 \div 8 =$ ☐   8 children can have ☐ each

3 $16 \div 4 =$ ☐   4 children can have ☐ each

4 $16 \div 2 =$ ☐   2 children can have ☐ each

5 $16 \div 1 =$ ☐   1 child can have ☐ each

Write down the answers.

1 $12 \div 2 =$ ☐   **2** $12 \div 3 =$ ☐   **3** $12 \div 4 =$ ☐   **4** $12 \div 6 =$ ☐

5 $12 \div 12 =$ ☐   **6** $9 \div 3 =$ ☐   **7** $10 \div 2 =$ ☐   **8** $10 \div 5 =$ ☐

9 $20 \div 2 =$ ☐   **10** $20 \div 4 =$ ☐   **11** $20 \div 5 =$ ☐   **12** $20 \div 10 =$ ☐

13 These cherries can be shared.

18 cherries in 1 bag

or ☐ cherries in 2 bags

or ☐ cherries in 3 bags

or ☐ cherries in 6 bags

Kilogrammes (kg)

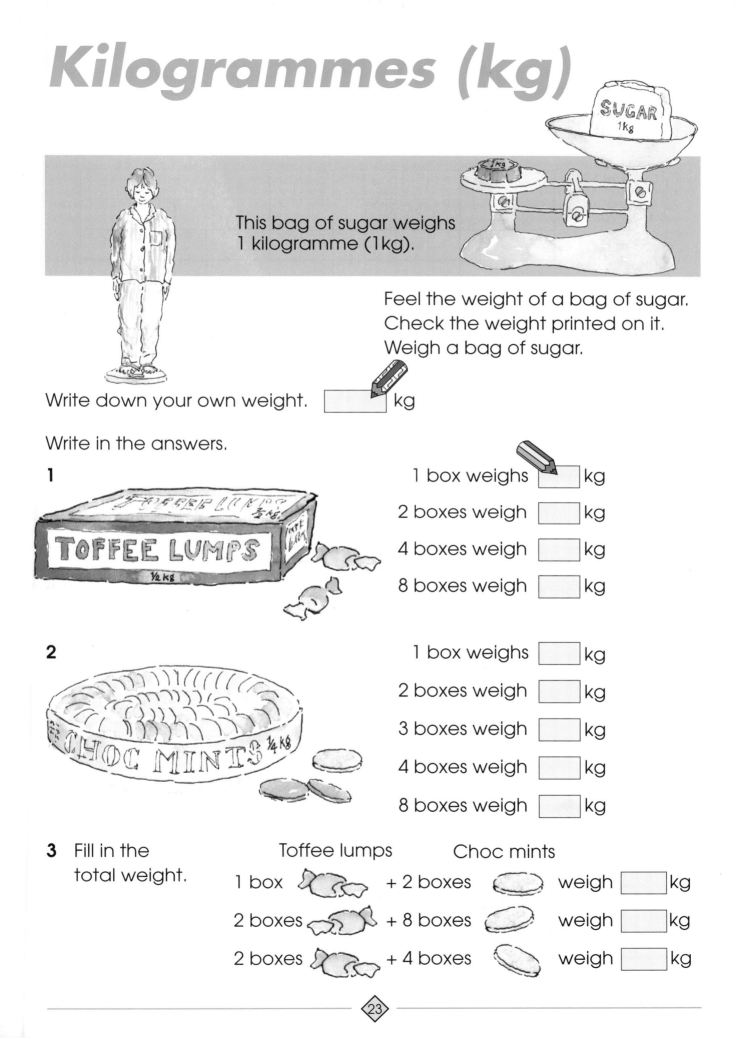

This bag of sugar weighs 1 kilogramme (1kg).

Feel the weight of a bag of sugar.
Check the weight printed on it.
Weigh a bag of sugar.

Write down your own weight. ☐ kg

Write in the answers.

1

TOFFEE LUMPS
½ kg

1 box weighs ☐ kg

2 boxes weigh ☐ kg

4 boxes weigh ☐ kg

8 boxes weigh ☐ kg

2

CHOC MINTS ¼ kg

1 box weighs ☐ kg

2 boxes weigh ☐ kg

3 boxes weigh ☐ kg

4 boxes weigh ☐ kg

8 boxes weigh ☐ kg

3 Fill in the total weight.

Toffee lumps		Choc mints		
1 box	+ 2 boxes		weigh	☐ kg
2 boxes	+ 8 boxes		weigh	☐ kg
2 boxes	+ 4 boxes		weigh	☐ kg

Table of threes

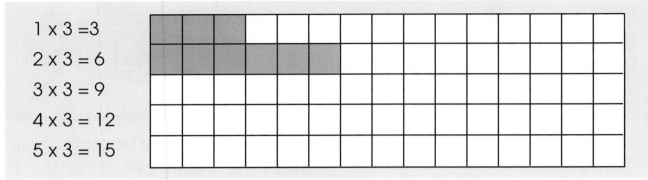

| 1 x 3 = 3 |
| 2 x 3 = 6 |
| 3 x 3 = 9 |
| 4 x 3 = 12 |
| 5 x 3 = 15 |

This graph of the 3 times table has been started for you.
Finish the graph up to 5 x 3.

Fill in the answers.

1 6 x 3 = ☐   **2** 7 x 3 = ☐   **3** 8 x 3 = ☐

4 9 x 3 = ☐   **5** 10 x 3 = ☐   **6** 18 ÷ 3 = ☐

7 12 ÷ 3 = ☐   **8** 21 ÷ 3 = ☐   **9** 3 ÷ 3 = ☐

Work these out.

1   5   **2**   11   **3**   20   **4**   12
      x 3   x 3   x 3   x 3
    ‾‾‾‾   ‾‾‾‾   ‾‾‾‾   ‾‾‾‾

5 21 ÷ 3 = ☐   **6** 30 ÷ 3 = ☐   **7** 27 ÷ 3 = ☐   **8** 33 ÷ 3 = ☐

9

1 cricket pitch needs 6 stumps.
Fill in this table.

pitches	1	2	3	4
stumps	6			

24

Saving

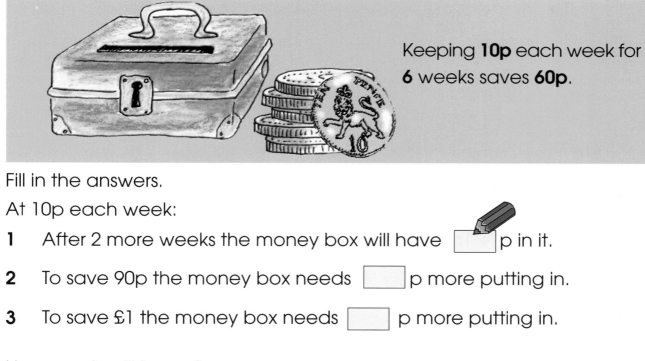

Keeping **10p** each week for **6 weeks** saves **60p**.

Fill in the answers.

At 10p each week:

1   After 2 more weeks the money box will have ⬚ p in it.

2   To save 90p the money box needs ⬚ p more putting in.

3   To save £1 the money box needs ⬚ p more putting in.

How much will I save?

1   10p each week for 5 weeks   ⬚ p

2   5p each week for 10 weeks   ⬚ p

3   20p each week for 5 weeks   £ ⬚

4   10p each week for 15 weeks £ ⬚

Your money box has £1 in it.

1   Put 10p in, take 20p out.
    You will have ⬚ p in it.

2   Put 50p in, take £1 out.
    You will have ⬚ p in it.

3   Put 40p in, take 60p out.
    You will have ⬚ p in it.

4   Put £2 in, take 30p out.
    You will have £ ⬚ in it.

Coins

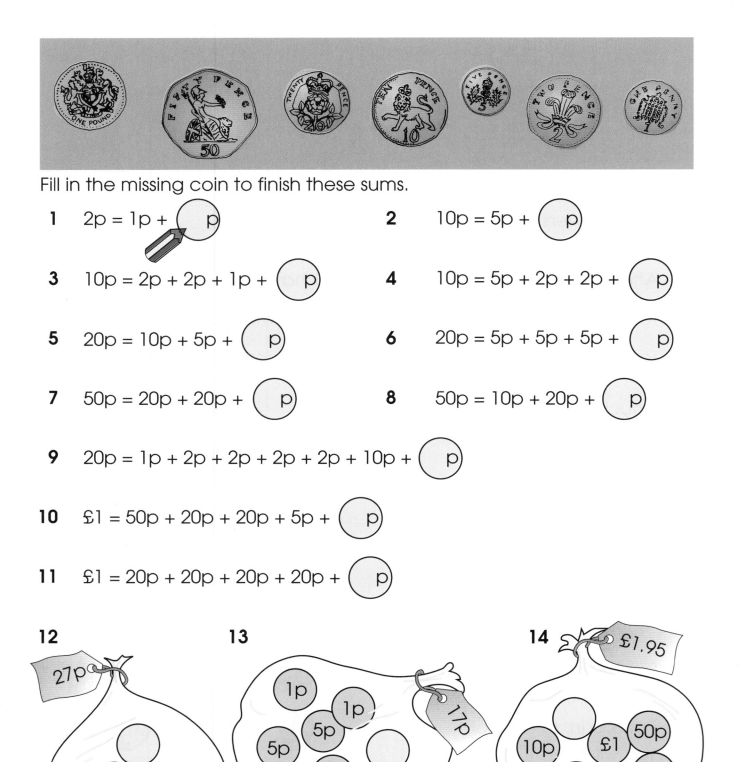

Fill in the missing coin to finish these sums.

1 2p = 1p + (_ p)

2 10p = 5p + (_ p)

3 10p = 2p + 2p + 1p + (_ p)

4 10p = 5p + 2p + 2p + (_ p)

5 20p = 10p + 5p + (_ p)

6 20p = 5p + 5p + 5p + (_ p)

7 50p = 20p + 20p + (_ p)

8 50p = 10p + 20p + (_ p)

9 20p = 1p + 2p + 2p + 2p + 2p + 10p + (_ p)

10 £1 = 50p + 20p + 20p + 5p + (_ p)

11 £1 = 20p + 20p + 20p + 20p + (_ p)

12 27p

13 17p

14 £1.95

Graphs

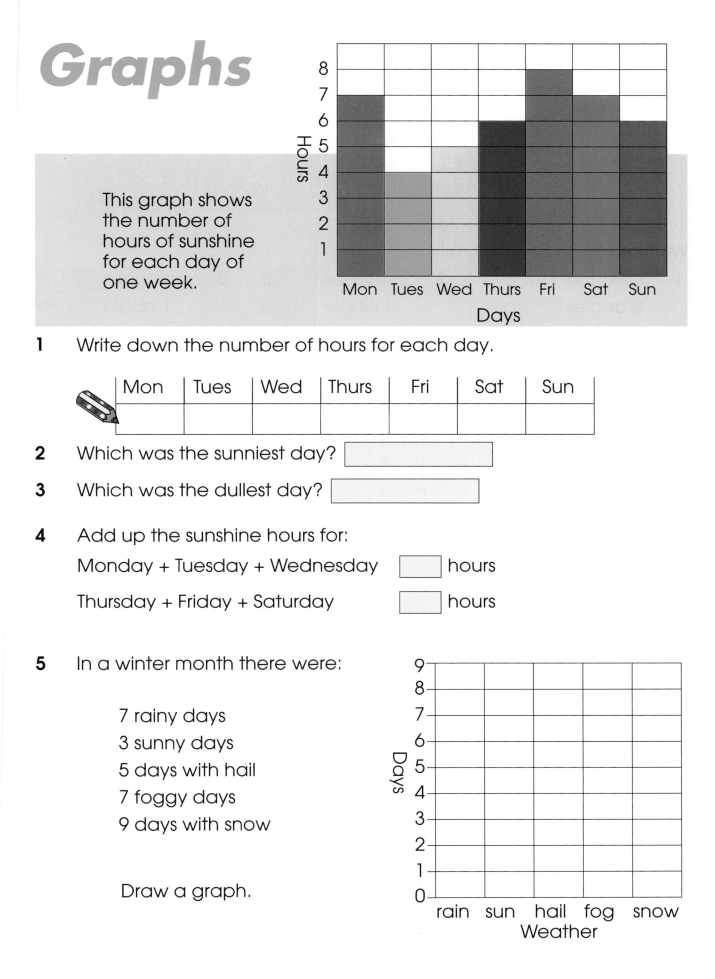

This graph shows the number of hours of sunshine for each day of one week.

1   Write down the number of hours for each day.

Mon	Tues	Wed	Thurs	Fri	Sat	Sun

2   Which was the sunniest day?

3   Which was the dullest day?

4   Add up the sunshine hours for:

Monday + Tuesday + Wednesday [   ] hours

Thursday + Friday + Saturday [   ] hours

5   In a winter month there were:

    7 rainy days
    3 sunny days
    5 days with hail
    7 foggy days
    9 days with snow

    Draw a graph.

The fruit shop

PINEAPPLES 50p each

JUICY ORANGES 10p each

BEST LEMONS 5p each

RIPE APPLES 6p each

Work out these shopping bills.

1 1 orange 10 p
    2 apples [ ] p
    3 lemons [ ] p
     Total [ ] p

2 2 oranges [ ] p
    1 apple [ ] p
    3 lemons [ ] p
     Total [ ] p

3 3 oranges [ ] p
    1 apple [ ] p
    2 lemons [ ] p
     Total [ ] p

4 5 oranges [ ] p
    1 pineapple [ ] p
     Total £ [ ]

5 10 lemons [ ] p
    1 pineapple [ ] p
     Total £ [ ]

6 5 oranges [ ] p
    10 lemons [ ] p
     Total £ [ ]

7 2 pineapples [ ] p
    10 apples [ ] p
     Total £ [ ]

8 10 lemons [ ] p
    10 oranges [ ] p
     Total £ [ ]

9 4 apples [ ] p
    5 lemons [ ] p
     Total [ ] p

Write more than, less than or the same as.

10 10 lemons cost [ ] 6 oranges

11 5 apples cost [ ] 3 oranges

12 1 pineapples costs [ ] 3 lemons

13 10 oranges cost [ ] 2 pineapples

How much change from [ONE POUND] will I get?

1 5 oranges. Change [ ] p

2 10 lemons. Change [ ] p

3 10 apples. Change [ ] p

4 8 apples. Change [ ] p

Squares and rectangles

Fill in the answers.

1 How many coloured squares make each rectangle?

How many of the squares are coloured?

green [ ] red [ ] blue [ ]

What fraction of each rectangle is coloured? $\dfrac{\boxed{}}{\boxed{}}$

2 Colour ¼ of each rectangle in different ways.

3 How many small squares make this large square? [ ]

How many make ½ of the large square? [ ]

How many make ¾ of the large square? [ ]

4 Colour ½ of this rectangle red and ⅓ of the rectangle blue.

Centimetres (cm) and metres (m)

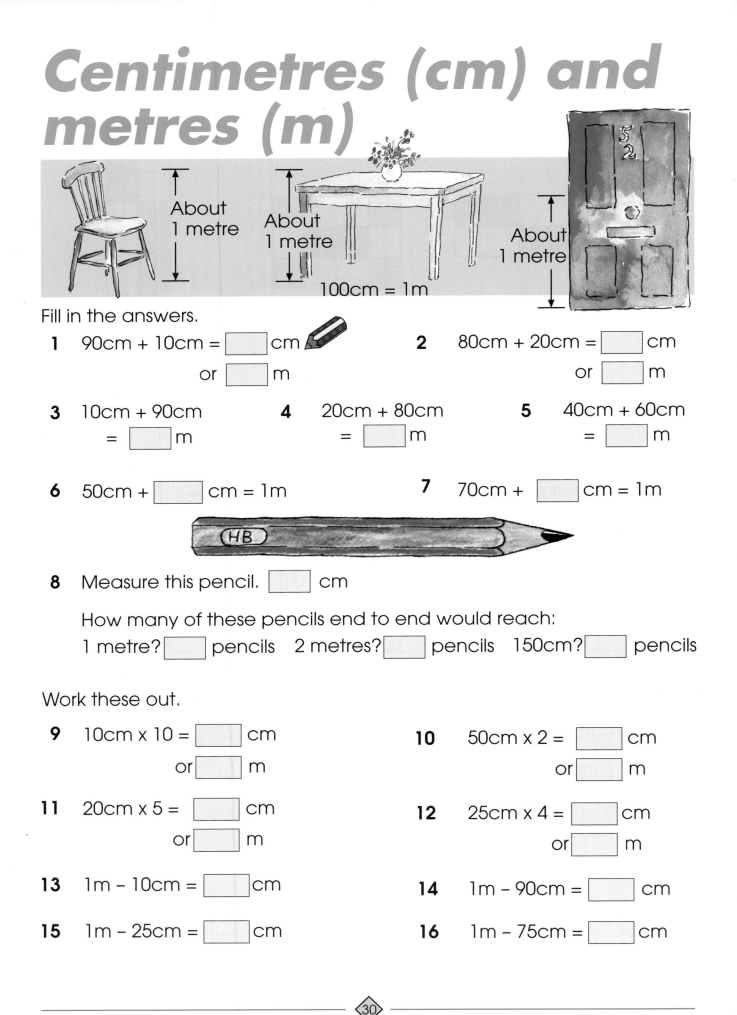

About 1 metre

About 1 metre

About 1 metre

100cm = 1m

Fill in the answers.

1 90cm + 10cm = ☐ cm
or ☐ m

2 80cm + 20cm = ☐ cm
or ☐ m

3 10cm + 90cm = ☐ m

4 20cm + 80cm = ☐ m

5 40cm + 60cm = ☐ m

6 50cm + ☐ cm = 1m

7 70cm + ☐ cm = 1m

8 Measure this pencil. ☐ cm

How many of these pencils end to end would reach:
1 metre? ☐ pencils   2 metres? ☐ pencils   150cm? ☐ pencils

Work these out.

9 10cm x 10 = ☐ cm
or ☐ m

10 50cm x 2 = ☐ cm
or ☐ m

11 20cm x 5 = ☐ cm
or ☐ m

12 25cm x 4 = ☐ cm
or ☐ m

13 1m – 10cm = ☐ cm

14 1m – 90cm = ☐ cm

15 1m – 25cm = ☐ cm

16 1m – 75cm = ☐ cm

Litres

1 litre will fill 8 small glasses.

This bottle contains 1 litre of Coola.

Put the missing numbers in the boxes.

1

will fill	1	2	3	4	5	6	7	8	bottles
	8								glasses

Mary invited friends to her party.

2

	From	1	2	3	bottles of Coola
8 children could have		1			glasses each.

3

	From	2	4	6	8	bottles of Coola
16 children could have		1				glasses each.

4   16 glasses could be filled from ☐ bottles.

24 glasses could be filled from ☐ bottles.

5

	½	1	1½	2	2½	bottles
would fill		8				glasses

1 bottle of Coola costs 80p.

6   The cost to fill 1 glass is ☐ p.

7   The cost to fill 2 glasses is ☐ p.

8   The cost to fill 10 glasses is £☐ .

Answers

To Parents: We have not provided *all* the answers here. We suggest that items to be coloured in on squares. lengths and graphs should be checked by you. In the case of activities where calculations are performed by your child, it would be good practice to get him/her to use a calculator to check the answers.

Page 2
1 17 seventeen 2 2 two 3 15 fifteen
1 29 2 66 3 41
4 111 5 200
1 twenty-eight 2 eighteen 3 forty-nine
4 ninety-four 5 fifty-five
6 seven hundred
1 41 2 200 3 20 4 94

Page 3
1 4,6,8,10 2 3,5,7,9 3 4,7,10,13
4 5,9,13,17 5 5,8,11,14

6
2		6	8
4	6	8	10
	8	10	

7
4	6	8	10
	6	8	10	12
	8	10	12	14

8
9	10	11	12	13
10	11	12	13	14
11	12	13	14	15
12	13	14	15	16
13	14	15	16	17

9
11	12	13	14	15
13	14	15	16	17
15	16	17	18	19
17	18	19	20	21
19	20	21	22	23

Page 4
1 50 2 75 3 80
4 100 5 100 6 150
7 120 8 95 9 95

Page 5
1 4 2 3 3 4, 4 4 4, 4
5 4 x 4 square 6 3 x 6 rectangle

Page 6
1 11 2 10 3 9 4 8 5 7 6 5
7 6 8 6 9 6 10 7 11 7 12 8
13 6 14 5 15 4 16 6 17 10 18 9
1 5 2 4 3 20 4 19 5 5 6 4
7 20 8 19 9 11 10 6 11 9 12 1

Page 7
1 40 2 22 3 103 4 121
5 50 6 122 7 150 8 222
1 21 2 60 3 63 4 24
5 28 6 40
1 40 2 40 3 90 4 100

Page 8
1 2 2 5 3 10 4 25
5 2,10 6 100 7 50 8 2
9 2 10 1 11 2 12 2
13 4 14 10 15 5

Page 9
1 12 2 21 3 12 4 12
1 18 2 18 3 18 4 118
5 108 6 8 7 4 8 19
9 2 10 99 11 101
1 9 2 4

Page 10
1 4 2 4 3 4 4 5
5 4 6 4 7 4 8 4,1
9 29 10 Wednesday 11 4, 6, 8, 10, 12, 14, 16, 18, 20, 22, 24, 26, 28, 30
12 3, 6, 9, 12, 15, 18, 21, 24, 27, 30

Page 11
1 12 2 8 3 + 4 −
5 19 6 − 7 − 8 21
9 0 10 + 11 + 12 1
13 − 14 + 15 − 16 −
17 7 18 7 19 7 20 7
1 +, +, + 2 +, +, − 3 +, −, + 4 −, +, −

Page 12
1 3, 6, 9, 15, 18, 21, 24, 30
2 4, 8, 12, 16, 20, 24, 28, 32, 36, 40
3 5, 10, 15, 20, 25, 30, 35, 40, 45, 50

4
2	4	6	8
6		18	24
10	20		40

5
0	1	3	5
0	3	9	15
0	5	15	25

6
4	8	12
8	16	24
12	24	36

7 5, 4, 20
8 6, 3, 18

Page 13
1 ⅗, ⅖ 2 ½, ½ 3 ½, ½

Page 14
1 10 2 15 3 8 4 12
5 0 6 9 7 9 8 12 9 0
10 6 + 12 + 21 = 39 11 9 + 18 + 24 = 51

Page 15
1–10 12 11 9 12 6 13 6
14 3 15 10 16 8 17 8
18 4 19 2 20 0

Page 16
1 10 past 9 2 9 o' clock 3 10 past 9, 10 to 9, ¼ past 9, ¼ to 9 4 ½ past 2, ¼ past 2, ¼ to 3, 25 past 2, 25 to 3
5 3 o'clock, 10 past 3, ¼ to 3, ½ past 3

Page 17
1 8, 8, 8, 2 6 3 6 4 12
5 12 6 20 7 20
8 4, 8, 12, 20, 24, 28, 32, 36, 40
9 5, 10, 15, 20, 25, 30, 35, 40, 45, 50

Page 18
1 9 2 16; 8, 4, 12 3 12 4 8
5 6 6 10 7 200, 100

Page 19
1 less, 10p 2 more, 10p 3 less, 20p
4 more, 20p 5 less, 40p 6 more, 30p
7 less, 50p 8 more, 50p 9 equal, 0
10 more, 1p 11 more, 5p

Page 20
1 5, 50 2 4, 40 3 6, 60 4 5½, 55
5 pink 6 yellow 7 10, 100 8 9, 90
9 11, 110 10 9½, 95 11 20½cm

Page 21
1 1 2 7 3
		3	
	14	28	35

4 14, 21, 28
5 1, 8, 15, 22, 29 6 2, 9, 16, 23, 30
7 31; 4, 3 8 11; 1, 4 9 17; 2, 3
10 18; 2, 4

Page 22
1 16 2 2 3 4 4 8 5 16
1 6 2 4 3 3 4 2 5 1
6 3 7 5 8 2 9 10
10 5 11 4 12 2 13 9, 6, 3

Page 23
1 ½, 1, 2, 4 2 ¼, ½, ¾, 1, 2 3 1, 3, 2

Page 24
1 18 2 21 3 24 4 27 5 30
6 6 7 4 8 7 9 1
1 15 2 33 3 60 4 36 5 7
6 10 7 9 8 11
9
	12	18	24

Page 25
1 80 2 30 3 40
1 50 2 50 3 1 4 1·50
1 90 2 50 3 80 4 2·70

Page 26
1 1 2 5 3 5 4 1 5 5
6 5 7 10 8 20 9 1 10 5
11 20 12 5 13 2 14 5

Page 27
1 7, 4, 5, 6, 8, 7, 6 2 Friday
3 Tuesday 4 16, 21

Page 28
1 12, 15, 37 2 20, 6, 15, 41
3 30, 6, 10, 46 4 1 5 1
6 1 7 1.60 8 1.50 9 49
10 less 11 same 12 more 13 same
1 50 2 50 3 40 4 52

Page 29
1 12; 6, 6, 6; ½ 3 16;8;12

Page 30
1 100; 1 2 100; 1 3 1 4 1
5 1 6 50 7 30
8 10; 10; 20; 15 9 100; 1 10 100; 1
11 100; 1 12 100; 1 13 90 14 10
15 75 16 25

Page 31
1 16, 24, 32, 40, 48, 56, 64
2
	2	3

3
	2	3	4

4 2, 3 5 4, 12, 16, 20 6 10
7 20 8 1

32